Also by Frank S. Rose

Illustrations for "*Herbal Medicine of the American Southwest*" by Charles W. Kane. 2006

"*Mountain Wildflowers of Southern Arizona*" published by the Arizona Sonoran Desert Museum. 2011

"*Mountain Trees of Southern Arizona*" published by the Arizona Sonoran Desert Museum. 2012

"*The Joy of Spiritual Living*" by Frank S. Rose and Bob Maginel published by the Swedenborg Foundation. 2014

"*The Joy of Spiritual Growth*" by Frank S. Rose and Bob Maginel published by the Swedenborg Foundation. 2015

"*The Art of Effective Preaching*" co-authored with son, Dr. Jeremy Rose. 2016

Illustrations for "*Bo and the Fly-away Kite*" by Virginia Wade Ames. 2016

Small Wonders

A Closer Look at Some Hard-to-See Flowers

Frank S. Rose

Hardy Perennial Press   Tucson AZ

Photo by Owen Rose

Camera equipment used:

Most pictures taken in the field without flash using a
Nikon D90 with a DX 18-105 mm lens using black velvet as a background.

Close-up photography done with:
Canon EOS Rebel T41 with macro photo lens - MP-E 65mm using a black velvet
background with fr Sigma EM-140D front end flash taken in the field.

Cover design by Owen Rose
Back cover photo by Dave Larson
All plant photos taken by Frank S. Rose.

ISBN 978-1-7325402-0-0

Hardy Perennial Press LLC
1645 W. Valencia Rd #109-154 Tucson Az 85746

Dedicated to Jim Verrier
Who has shown and taught me much.

Small Wonders

Plants put on quite a show in order to ensure pollination and the continued health of their offspring. From the perspective of human beings, certain plants seem designed to please them, a situation that is made even more plausible by the proliferation of cultivated plants to adorn our homes and gardens. But a great many plants are designed to attract very small pollinators, and their flowers are therefore quite small - you might even say invisible. And then there are those that are pollinated by the wind and do not need to put any energy into conspicuous displays. Some are visible flowers that are worth a closer look.

Flower guides, including my own "Mountain Wildflowers", tend to focus on the flowers that are easily seen. What of those that we pass by without a glance? It turns out that there are hundreds, even thousands, of them. They come in all kinds of categories - small plants with small flowers (the so-called belly flowers), large plants with small flowers, composites where the inflorescence looks like one flower but might contain scores or even hundreds of individual flowers, clusters of flowers where the cluster is noticeable but the single flowers are in a sense unseen and so on.

In this book plants are arranged according to the usual botanical divisions, starting with the distinction between angiosperms and gymnosperms, then monocots and eudicots; and the bulk of the book by family, genus and species.

The pictures in circles show the flower at greatest magnification. The tiny icon near it indicates an approximation of its actual size. Flowers that are 2 millimeters or smaller are represented by a small dot.

In this book we categorize plants as low, mid or high elevation. Low includes the Sonoran Desert and up to 4,500 feet. Mid is 4,500 to 6,000 feet. High is 6,000 to 9,000 feet. Blooming times are very approximate as Spring, Summer and Fall. In some cases I have grouped a number of plants of the same genus on one page to aid in identifying them.

For sedges, reeds, trees and grasses I include just a few examples to give an idea of what their reproductive parts look like.

There are a number of plants with nearly invisible flowers that are not included here - they are not showy or interesting enough.

CONTENTS

FLOWERING PLANTS – MONOCOTS 183

GYMNOSPERMS 195

The Angiosperms (Flowering plants)

Angiosperms are seed-bearing vascular plants. Vascular means something that has vessels for conveying fluids. Angio means vessel. Sperm means seed. The name means - a plant having seeds in an ovary. A Cotyledon is the primary or rudimentary leaf of the embryo of seed plants.

Acanthaceae - Acanthus Family
Carlowrightia arizonica - Arizona Wrightwort
This is a low elevation plant. The flowers come out before the mass of leaves shown in the middle picture. The absence of leaves makes the plant look dead but the flowers more visible. It is very easy to pass by this plant and not even notice that it is in bloom. Flowers mostly in March to May. The fruits have a rather interesting shape.

Justicia longii - Siphonoglossa
This is a low elevation plant that blooms from Spring into Fall. The flowers open in the evening and close during the morning. At the tip of the flower in the top right picture there is a tiny red spider.

Atriplex canescens - Four-wing Saltbush
This evergreen shrub grows mostly in mid elevations and blooms most of
the growing season. The flowers are difficult to spot on separate male and
female plants. Top left you can see the pollen, so those flowers are male.
The female flowers, top right, are more difficult to spot. In the bottom
picture, a female plant is on the left and a male on the right. The middle
picture shows a cluster of the 4-wing fruit.

Chenopodium fremontii - Fremont's Goosefoot

This mid to high elevation plant has leaves shaped like a goose's foot, hence the name. It blooms in late Summer and Fall. The flowers are very small, and though I had seen the plant many times in my mountain walks, it was only recently that I photographed its unusual flowers. The middle picture shows a leaf with a stalk with flower buds along it.

Dysphania graveolens - Fetid Goosefoot

This mostly high elevation plant has leaves shaped a little like oaks. It has quite a strong odor which I find very pleasant, in spite of its name. The flowers are very small and bloom in late Summer and Fall. It turns a beautiful red in the Fall as shown in the middle picture.

9

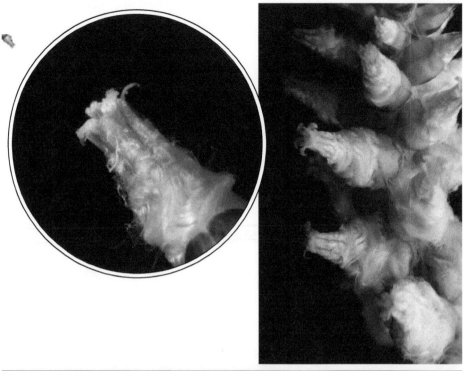

Froelichia arizonica - Snake Cotton

The flowers on this plant are quite small, just like little gold dots at the end of each of the protuberances. It grows in the mid range, blooming from June into Fall. The lower picture shows a plant blown over by the wind.

Gomphrena caespitosa - Tufted Globe Amaranth, Ball Clover
This mid-elevation plant lies fairly flat on the ground, blooming from
Spring to late Summer. Flowers are quite small, surrounded by white
bracts. One picture shows its fluffy white fruits which are much more noticeable than the actual flowers.

11

Amaranthaceae - Amaranth Family

Amaranthus sonorae - Globe Amaranth
This is another plant where the actual flowers are very small and rarely seen. It grows in the mid range, blooming in late Summer and Fall. As can be seen in these pictures we enjoy it without noticing the actual blooms since they are surrounded by bracts, some white and some deep pink. When it turns to seed it becomes very fluffy.

Guilleminea densa - Matweed
I have often stepped on this plant. It is hard to avoid since it forms huge mats on dirt roads and trails. It is a mid elevation plant and is in bloom from Spring into Fall. Its flowers are very nearly invisible without the use of some kind of lens.

Amaranthaceae - Amaranth Family

Salsola tragus - Russian Thistle
This non-native low elevation plant has somewhat diaphanous flowers
which can range from pale yellow to deep red, and bloom in late Summer
and Fall. It is also known as Tumbleweed, since it forms a ball of branches
attached by a single stem which, when it breaks off, rolls as the wind
blows, depositing seeds as it goes.

Tidestromia lanuginosa - Woolly Tidestromia
I first met this plant in the grounds of Sunrise Chapel in Tucson. I thought it might be one of the Euphorbias. It forms a fairly large mat, with stems red on top and green underneath. This is a low elevation plant that blooms in late Summer into the Fall. Its leaves are very soft, hence the common name.

Bowlesia incana - Hairy Bowlesia
For a number of years this small plant has filled in a solid patch of foliage, about seven by two feet, in our back yard (shown in the picture above.) The picture with a penny gives some idea of the size of the whole plant. More or less in the center of the stalk a cluster of tiny flowers forms. It blooms in the valley from February to May. The leaf has a distinctive shape.

Daucus pusilllus - American Wild Carrot
This low to mid elevation plant blooms in Spring. Its leaves tend to surround the flower heads, making the flowers difficult to see. As its name
suggests, it is related to the cultivated carrot (*Daucus carota* subsp. sati-
vus). The Latin word, *pusillus* means *small, weak or insignificant.*

Heracleum lanatum - Cow Parsnip
This is one of the largest plants on the mountain, growing taller than
people in high elevations along streams. It blooms in late Spring and early
Summer. The flower heads are quite visible, but it requires a closer look to
see how assymeterical each individual flower in the cluster is.

Lomatium nevadense - Biscuit Root

This mid elevation plant blooms in very early Spring. The flower head in the picture is about two inches across, so individual flowers are very small indeed. Their petals are curled, and the anthers (purple) start by being tucked in between the petals. Then they extend upward as in the other picture of an individual flower.

Osmorhiza depauperata - Sweet Cicely
This plant grows high on the mountain and is never far from water. It blooms more or less all year except for the Winter months. As you can see from my thumb, the leaves are reasonably large, and the flowers are tiny. Of special interest is the mature fruit that looks like some kind of medieval lance.

Pseudocympoterus montanus - Alpine False Springparsley
This plant mostly grows high in the mountains. It can bloom any time in
Spring, Summer or Fall. Plants are around a foot tall with yellow flower
clusters. The mid right picture shows the rarer red variation.

Apiaceae - Carrot Family

Spermolepis echinata - Scale Seed
This plant with very small flowers grows at mid elevation in early Spring
on north-facing slopes, making it easy to miss. Some years I have missed it
entirely. Other years I have seen it carpeting the hillsides.

Yabea microcarpa - False Carrot
Like Scale Seed, *Spermolepis echinata*, this is an early bloomer (sometimes as early as February) growing at mid elevations in damp soil. Some
years it covers the ground, almost like grass.

Apocynum androsaemifolium - Spreading Dogbane
This is a mostly-Summer blooming, high elevation, plant. It has a milky
sap that is acrid. The word *bane* means *harmful* or *poisonous.*

Asclepias tuberosa - Butterfly Milkweed
This is a mid elevation plant that can bloom as early as May and continue into Fall. It is a highly visible and beautiful flowering plant. We include it to show a close-up of an individual flower. Its shape is typical of others in the milkweed family.

25

Cynanchum arizonicum - Arizona Swallow-wort
This is a desert plant that climbs over other plants. It is mostly a Summer
plant and has yellow flowers and small but long fruits.

Funastrum cynanchoides ssp. heterophyllum - Hartweg's Twinevine,
Climbing Milkweed
There are a number of climbing Milkweeds. This one grows in mid elevations, and blooms most of the time from Spring to Fall. Flower clusters are
visible, but easy to overlook. Individual flowers are worth a closer look.

Matelea parviflora - Smallflower Milkvine, Smallflower Milkweed Vine
This flower qualifies as "Invisible" because of its tiny size and dark color.
The plant may be seen climbing on Saguaros (*Carnegiea gigantea*) at low
elevations, blooming Spring and Summer.

Aralia racemosa - American Spikenard
This is a high elevation plant with large flower clusters in the Summer.
Individual flowers are quite tiny. The fruits turn a deep purple color.

Aristolochiaceae - Birthwort Family

Aristolochia watsonii - Pipevine, Watson's Dutchman's Pipe
The bottom picture shows a Pipevine lying on the ground, hard to distinguish from surrounding foliage. This is a low to mid elevation plant. It can bloom Spring, Summer or Fall. The middle right picture shows part of a plant. Its sap is toxic, and the Pipevine swallowtail takes advantage of this by ingesting it to make itself and its larvae repugnant to predators. The butterfly lays its eggs on the underside of the plant. When they hatch they consume the leaves until virtually nothing is left, and then the plant regenerates from its generous roots.

ASTERACEAE

We now come to one of the largest families of flowering plants, Asteraceae (formerly known as Compositae, or Composite family). The word "aster" comes from the Greek meaning a star, referring to the way that many in this family have a central part with radiating lines. The other word, composite, refers to the fact that what seems at first glance to be one flower is a composite of many flowers, sometimes hundreds of them.

With sunflower-types of flowers, the ones in the center are called "disc flowers" and those radiating out are called "ray flowers". They look like petals, but each "petal" is actually a complete flower. Disc flowers are often in a spiral. The flowers open in sequence, so that at any one time there may be three different forms: a flower bud, an opened flower and a pollinated flower.

Here is an example, Desert Marigold. The plant's botanical name is Baileya multiradiata, meaning the "Bailey plant with many ray flowers". I took one apart and spread it out. There were about 200 disc flowers and 50 ray flowers. The three pictures below show the different forms of the disc flowers, and one ray flower. Because each flower head has hundreds of flowers, the flowers stay in bloom a very long time. Each flower has to be visited by pollinators separately.

Not all composites have this particular structure, but all have multiple flowers in their inflorescence. Since the Aster family is one of the largest in the world, there are thousands of them. We have selected a few for their special interest.

Disc bud   Disc flower   Ray flower

Asteraceae - Composite or Sunflower Family

Achillea millefolum var. lanulosa - Yarrow
This is a high elevation plant with flower clusters that bloom in Summer and Fall. Each individual flower has a cluster of its own. The picture in the circle shows an individual disc flower. The flowers are usually white. Once in a while you can see pink ones as in the right middle picture above

32

Ageratina herbaceae - Fragrant Snakeroot
This is a high elevation plant that blooms in Fall. The botanical name, "ageratina", means non-aging, referring to the way the flowers persist. The left middle picture shows red filaments packed between each flower bud. The white stamens sticking out give it a feathery look.

Ambrosia ambrosioides - Canyon Ragweed

This low elevation plant grows very large. The flowers are barely visible as you can see in the left middle picture. The male flowers, top left, are like miniature sunflowers. To its right is the female flower. The branch in the middle left picture has male flowers at the tips and female flowers lower down the stalk.

Ambrosia confertiflora - Slimleaf Bursage
This is a low and mid elevation plant that is very abundant in places like Molino Basin. It can bloom in Spring, Summer or Fall. Walking by, it is hard to notice whether it is in bloom or not.

Ambrosia deltoidea - Triangleleaf Bursage
This low elevation evergreen plant has somewhat triangular leaves. It blooms in Winter and into early Summer. The picture top left shows a flower head with male flowers. Top right is a female flower. In the left middle picture you can see a string of male flowers; middle right shows male flowers, with one female flower lower down. This is a very common plant in the desert.

Artemsia dracunculus - False Tarragon
This is a mid elevation plant that blooms in Summer and Fall. The flowers are quite small, though the plant is fairly large, sometimes as tall as six feet.

Artemesia ludoviciana - White Sagebrush, Wormwood, Silver Sage
This species has a number of sub-species. It grows from mid to high elevations, blooming Summer and into the Fall. Its leaves have a distinctive fragrance.

Baccharis salicifolia - Seep Willow, Mule-Fat
This is a low to mid elevation plant that lives in stream beds. It blooms
Summer and Fall. There are separate male and female plants (dioecious).
In the pictures above, the left is male and the right is female. It can be
taller than a person. The botanical name suggests that its leaves look like a
willow.

39

Bidens leptocephala - Fewflower Beggarticks
This mid-elevation plant blooms in Summer and Fall. It has fairly small flower heads. Each head has mostly disc flowers. The top left photograph shows it with two ray flowers. "Bidens" means "two teeth" and refers to the fact that each fruit ends in two teeth, as seen in the top right picture.

These are eight of the *Brickellias* (Brickelbush) in the Santa Catlina mountains. 1-5 and 8 are mid elevation, 6 and 7 are high. Plants are generally large and the flowers not very noticeable. #4 blooms most of the year. The rest bloom mostly in late Summer and Fall. They are all Brickelbushes. Reading from the top le*ft:*

1) B. amplexicaulis - Earleaf*; 2) B. betonicifolia* - Betonyleaf*; 3) B. californica* - California*; 4) B. coulteri* - Coulter's; *5) B. floribunda* - Chihuahuan*; 6) B. grandiflora* - Tasselflower; *7) B. rusbyi* - Stinking (also the landscape picture), 8) B.*venosa* - Veiny.

Carminatia tenuiflora - Plume Weed

This is a mid elevation plant with flowers that are tiny and rarely seen. It blooms in the Fall. It is better known from its fruit, as the name suggests.

Cirsium neomexicanum - New Mexico Thistle
This and other thistles have only disc flowers. The top left is one flower head taken apart. In the circle we see an individual flower. This is a mid elevation plant that blooms most of the year.
Bottom right is the flower head of Wheeler's Thistle (*Cirsium wheeleri*) that grows in higher elevations. Because it is not one but many flowers it can host a number of insects at once.

43

Asteraceae - Composite or Sunflower Family

Conyza canadensis - Horseweed

This is a tall mid-and-high elevation plant with tiny flowers. It is a late Summer and Fall bloomer. The middle right picture shows a couple of fruits mixed in with the flowers, illustrating how much more noticeable the fruits are.

Dyssodia papposa - Fetid Marigold
This is a rarely seen high elevation plant. Plants are about six inches tall and bloom in Summer. Note the yellow glands on the bracts and leaves in the close-up picture. The name *fetid* refers to the odor from these glands.

Asteraceae - Composite or Sunflower Family

Galinsoga parviflora - Galinsoga, Gallant Soldier
This is a high elevation plant. I have seen it mostly in the Catalina mountains on Mt. Bigelow, Oracle Ridge and Incerator Ridge in late Summer. The plant is a foot or two tall, and the flowers quite small. The fact that its botanical name is the same as the common name tells you it is rarely noticed.

Guardiola platyphylla - Guardiola, Apache Plant
This is a mid elevation plant that likes to grow on rocks near water. Its leaves are flat, as the name indicates. It can bloom almost any time of the year except for the coldest winter months. The middle right picture shows how the inflorescences can vary.

47

Hieracium carneum - Huachuca Hawkweed
This mid elevation plant is a Summer bloomer. It looks so much like grass that when it is not in flower it is almost indistinguishable from the surrounding vegetation. Its flowering time is a fairly short portion of the middle of the day.

Hieracium lemmonii (H. crepidispermum) - Lemmon's Hawkweed
This is a fairly tall high elevation plant with flowers that hang down in
clusters, as in the upper left picture. It blooms mid-Summer into Fall.
Because the flowers face downwards it is easy to pass by without noticing
it is in bloom. The stalk and leaves are very hairy.

49

Hymenoclea (Ambrosia) monogyra - Singlewhorl Burrobrush
This is a mostly low elevation plant with at least one plant in Gordon
Hirabayashi at about 5000 feet. It can grow very large, up to eight feet
tall, and fills some of the washes in Tucson and other places. The close-
up picture shows buds and one flower in bloom. Top right picture shows
leaves and flower buds. The one below it shows leaves and fruit. Below
that is the fruit which turns translucent with age.

Hymenoclea (Ambrosia) salsola - Cheesebush, Burrobrush
This low elevation, Spring-blooming shrub is abundant in Sabino Canyon. Like others in this genus, the male (shown) and female flowers (not
shown) are on the same branch. The top left picture is a close-up of the
fruit.

Hymenothrix wrightii - Wright's Thimblehead, Wright Beeflower
This is a high elevation plant with conspicuous flower clusters that bloom some of the Summer and much of the Fall. The petals are white, but the style is dark purple, which gives the flowers a gray cast. The circle shows a single flower from a cluster. It grows in abundance along Catalina Highway.

Laennecia schiedeana - Pineland Horseweed
This is a Fall-blooming high elevation plant. Plants can be tall, with flowers that are tiny and rarely noticed. It is easier to spot when it's in fruit as in the top left picture. These plants are abundant in the mountains.

Parthenium incanum - Mariola

This low elevation subshrub blooms from Summer into Fall. The flower
heads (top right) contain two kinds of flowers, shown in the closeup.

Porophyllum gracile - Slender Poreleaf, Odora
This is mostly a low elevation perennial plant that blooms much of the
year. It has a pungent smell. Its leaves can be used in salad. Flower heads
are very elegant but are so small they are rarely noticed. The flower head
(in the circle) consists of many flowers.

Ratibida columnifera - Mexican Hat

This is a non-native plant growing in mid elevations. It blooms Summer and Fall. The red form looks black at a distance. Some plants have yellow petals. Zooming in on the column, you can see that it is dotted with tiny individual flowers capped with pollen stars.

Schkuhria pinnata - Pinnate False Threadleaf
This is another rarely-seen mid to high elevation plant. It can be up to a
few feet tall, and blooms in the Fall.

Tagetes micrantha - Licorice Marigold
This tiny high elevation plant can blanket an area as seen above. Plants are a few inches high and bloom in late Summer and Fall. It usually has one or two ray flowers. I have splayed the flower head out to show a number of the disc flowers. Its leaves taste and smell like licorice.

Amsinckia intermedia - Common Fiddleneck
This grows in low and mid elevations. It is a medium sized plant with
very hairy leaves and bracts. The inflorescence is curled like a fiddleneck,
blooming from Winter into Spring. The flowers are yellow with a deep
orange blush.

Boraginaceae - Borage Family

Cryptantha pterocarya - Wingnut Cryptantha, Wing-nut Popcorn Flower
"Cryptantha" means "hidden flower". There are a number of different species
all of which have relatively small flowers often covered with hairs. This mid-
elevation Spring bloomer has fruit in the shape of a wing, shown in the lower left
corner. Its flowers are some of the smallest of the Cryptanthas.

Hackelia pinetorum - Livermore Stickseed
This high elevation plant is found at the top of the Ski Area in the Catalina
Mountains. It blooms in late Summer and Fall. The plants are quite large, and the
little blue flowers come at the end of the stalks.

Boraginaceae - Borage Family

Harpagonella palmeri - Palmer's Grappling Hook
This very small desert plant blooms in Spring and is noted for its fruits in
the shape of hooks.

Lappula occidentalis - Flatspine Stickseed
This is a low elevation, Springtime plant. Note particularly the fruits with all their points (middle left picture).

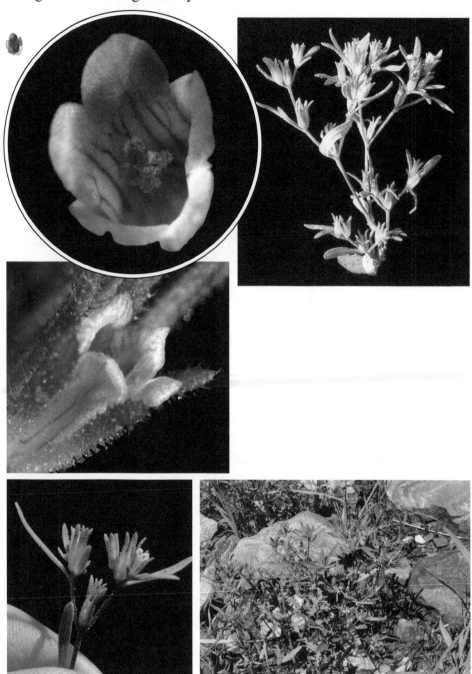

Nama dichotomum- Wishbone Fiddleleaf, Forked Purple Mat
This is a high elevation plant which is a late Summer bloomer. You can see how small it is from the picture with me holding it. The flowers are tiny with interesting purple streaks.

Pectocarya recurvata - Curvenut Combseed, Arch-nutted Comb Bur :
Pectocarya platycarpa - Broadfruit Combseed, Broad-nutted Comb Bur.
Here are two low elevation small plants that bloom in Spring. On the left
is *P. recurvata* with its curved fruit. The flower and fruit on the right are *P.
platycarpa* with fruit that is less curved.

Pholistoma auritum - Blue Fiestaflower
This low to mid elevation vine is floppy and has pale blue flowers. It blooms in Winter and Spring. The lower right picture shows the leaves and flower buds.

Plagiobothrys arizonicus - Blood Weed, Arizona Popcorn Flower
This is another low elevation Spring flower. The sap is red, as can be seen
from the leaf picture above, hence one of its common names.

Tiquilia canescens - Woody Crinklemat

This is a very widespread desert subshrub, growing at low elevations. It seems that it can bloom almost any month from Spring to Fall. The flowers are small and hard to see. The name "canescens" means covered with white hair which acts as a boundary layer reducing evaporation from wind and heat.

The Mustard Family is best known for its edible plants like Cabbages, Cauliflower, Mustard and Turnip. Their flowers tend to be rather small with four petals and four sepals. The one below is included because I once found what I thought was a new plant and it turned out to be *Arabis perennans*. It had been invaded by a fungus (*Puccinia monoica*) which changed the shape of the leaves and covered them with yellow dots, so that the leaves look like flowers (there were no flowers on it at all.) The idea is that the "flowers" would attract a pollinator which would spread the fungus instead of spreading the plant.

Arabis perennans – Perennial Rock Cress

This is a mid-elevation plant that blooms in Spring. Though its flowers are not particularly small they are still worth a closer look. The three lower pictures show 1) the whole plant infected, so that it looks like a totally different species, 2) part of it in my hand, 3) the infected leaves covered with yellow dots that make it look like a flower. Note that the real flowers come in purple and white.

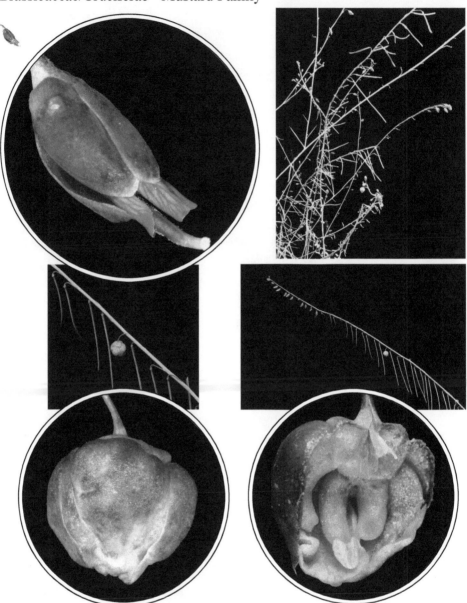

Pennellia longifolia - Longleaf Mock Thelypody
This is a high elevation Summer plant. After the flower is pollinated, it sends out a shoot that elongates and becomes the fruit, full of seeds. These hang down like wind chimes. Note a different kind of flower in the middle row. This is called cleistogamic. Some plants, to ensure reproduction, have flowers that are totally enclosed (and so invisible to us). These are self-pollinating. The bottom pictures show one closed, and then cut open to see the reproductive parts. Violets can have similar cleistogamic flowers. (See page 181)

Nemacladus glanduliferus - Glandular Threadplant
This is a tiny low elevation plant that blooms in Spring. The stems are
very thin, and the flowers well worth a closer look. This is one of my
favorite "invisible" flowers.

71

Campanulaceae - Bellflower Family

Triodanis holzingeri - Holzinger's Venus' Looking-glass
This is a water-loving mid elevation plant which blooms in Spring. It is
sometimes hard to find since it grows, usually single-stalked, among other
plants. Its bluish-purple flowers are quite attractive. Just a few flowers on
the stalk are open at any given time.

Cerastium brachypodum - Shortstalk Chickweed
This is a low elevation plant that likes to grow along stream beds. It
blooms in Spring and Summer. Its botanical name refers to its relatively
short stalk.

Drymaria leptophylla - Canyon Drymary
This is a very small, high elevation plant that blooms late Summer and Fall. It forms mats of foliage that almost look like grass cover. The leaf picture is to help distinguish it from *Drymaria molluginea* (p.75).

Drymaria molluginea - Slimleaf Drymary
This is another small, high elevation plant that blooms late Summer and
Fall. It is similar to the other Drymary (p.74), but the leaves are thinner.

Silene antirrhina - Sleepy Silene, Sleepy Catchfly
This is a low elevation Spring plant whose flowers don't open until about noon, hence the name "sleepy." The stems have a red patch that is very sticky to catch flies and other insects. The plant can be up to a foot tall, but is rarely noticed because of the fairly small flowers and the short time they are open.

Evolvulus alsinoides - Slender Dwarf Morning-glory
This low to mid elevation plant is very much like *Evolvulus arizonicus* (Arizona Blue Eyes) but the flowers are smaller. It blooms from Spring to Fall. Flowers are usually blue but sometimes white.

Cornaceae - Dogwood Family

Cornus sericea - Redosier Dogwood
This a high elevation shrub that blooms in late Spring and early Summer.
It grows along stream beds. After flowering it produces white fruit.

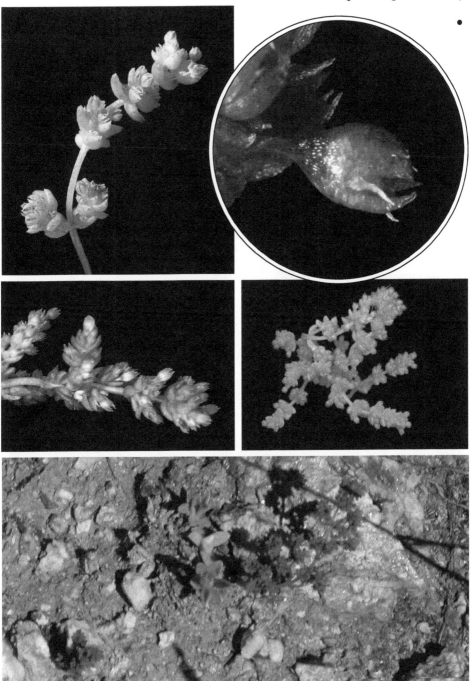

Crassula connata - Sand Pygmyweed
This mid elevation plant lies flat on the ground and is mostly red. It is a
Spring bloomer.

Crassulaceae - Stonecrop or Orpine Family

Graptopetalum rusbyi - San Francisco River Leatherpetal
This mid elevation plant grows in north facing rocky areas near stream beds and is a late Spring bloomer. It is a succulent. In the lower picture my friend is looking at the plant, which is spectacular yet very hard to see.

Sedum cockerellii - Cockerell's Stonecrop
This evergreen high elevation plant grows on north-facing stony areas and
blooms in late Summer and Fall.

Cucurbitaceae - Cucumber Family

Marah gilensis - Gila Manroot, Wild Cucumber
This mid elevation vine drapes itself over other plants, and blooms in early
Spring. It has small pale yellow flowers, and round spikey fruits.

Cuscuta applanata - Gila River Dodder
This low to mid elevation vine is parasitic on other plants. It blooms in
Fall. A seed that germinates has only 5 to 10 days to attach to a host plant
if it is to survive. Its leaves are negligible since it uses the chlorophyll of
the host plant.

Euphorbiaceae - Spurge Family

Acalypha neomexicana - New Mexico Copperleaf
This plant ranges from low to high elevation. It is a Fall bloomer. The flowers are hidden and unusual. The foliage turns red in the Fall, giving it the name "Copperleaf".

Argythamnia neomexicana - New Mexico Silverbush
This is a low elevation plant that blooms in Spring, Summer and Fall.
Note the distinctive fruit consisting of three parts.

Euphorbiaceae - Spurge Family

Here are six spurges, all Chamaesyce. The plants generally lie flat on the ground. Reading from the top le*ft: 1) C. arizonica* - Arizona Sandmat; *2) C. capitellata* - Head Sandmat*; 3) C. florida* - Chiricahua Mountain Sandmat; *4) C. melanadenia* - Red-gland Spurge; 5) C. *polycarpa* - Smallseed Sandmat; 6) C. *setiloba:* - Yuma Sandmat - which is also pictured at the bottom of the page. All are low elevation except #4 - Red-gland Spurge, which is mid-elevation.

Croton fruticulosus - Bush Croton
A low elevation plant which blooms in Spring and Summer. It can form a
very wide mat two or three feet high.

Euphorbia antisyphilitica - Candelilla
This low elevation plant grows in great clumps of leafless stalks. The clump can be up to three feet high. It blooms on and off throughout the year, mostly Spring and Summer. It has a waxy skin, and its milky sap has been used to treat sexually transmitted diseases.

Euphorbia spathulata (alta) - Warty Spurge
This is a mid to high elevation plant mostly blooming in Summer. It grows
to more than a foot tall. Its flowers are small and hard to see. The plant is
named for its fruit (top left picture).

Euphorbia yaquiana - Hairy Mojave Spurge
This is mostly a mid elevation plant growing along stream beds. Its flowers are yellow, and its leaf groupings are a good means of identification. It forms a substantial clump.

Jatropha cardiophylla - Heartleaf Limberbush
This is a low elevation plant mostly blooming in Spring and early Summer. Its branches are highly flexible. The small flowers are a pale yellow.

Euphorbiaceae - Spurge Family

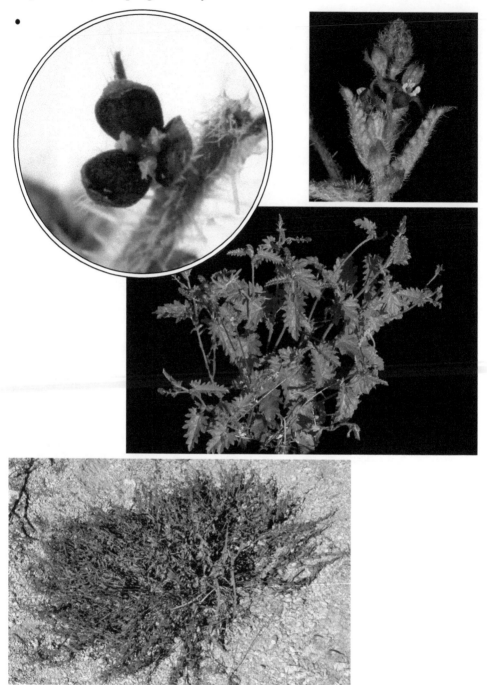

Tragia nepetifolia - Catnip Noseburn
This low to mid elevation plant grows in damp places, usually along stream beds and blooms most of the flowering year. The leaves can irritate the skin.

Amorpha californica - California False Indigo Bush
There are two False Indigo Bushes in the Catalina Mountains, A. *califor-nica* (growing fairly high in the mountain) and A. *fruticosa* (growing more in mid elevations.) This one is a Summer bloomer. "Amorpha" means "formless" referring to the unusual shape of the flowers.

Dalea filiformis - Sonoran Prairie Clover
This mid to high elevation plant flowers in Fall. Plants are only about six
inches tall with thread-like leaves. The flowers themselves are very small.

Dalea neomexicana - Downy Prairie Clover
This is a low elevation plant. It flowers most of the year but primarily in
Spring. Quite attractive fruits (middle left) give it a downy look and are
much more evident than the flowers.

Dalea pogonathera - Bearded Prairie Clover
This low elevation plant flowers most of the year. The plant can be a few feet tall, with small flowers radiating out from a center. The fruit is interesting.

Dalea polygonoides - Sixweeks Prairie Clover
This high elevation plant blooms in Fall. It is similar to *Dalea filiformis*
(p.94), but the flowers are white or blue whereas the other has red flowers.
It may be found in fairly large patches, like the picture just above, sometimes mixed in with *Dalea filiformis*.

97

Fabaceae - Bean Family

Dalea pringlei - Pringle's Prairie Clover
This low elevation plant flowers much of the year. The flowers are hard
to spot in the middle picture, but they are there (marked with white arrows). Recently I found a plant growing in Molino Basin, so it seems to be
blooming higher on the mountain than before.

Dalea wrightii - Wright's Prairie Clover
This low elevation plant is noteworthy in having yellow flowers (it is unusual for daleas to have yellow flowers). It blooms in the Fall.

Desmodium procumbens - Western Trailing Tickclover
The flowers on this mid elevation plant are white or pale pink. It is a late Summer and early Fall bloomer. The fruit sequences have a twist to them.

Desmodium psilocarpum - Santa Cruz Island Ticktrefoil, Tick Clover
This low to mid elevation plant flowers in late Summer and Fall. The
plants can form fairly large masses, as in this photograph taken in Bear
Canyon in the Catalina Mountains. It likes to be near water.

Desmodium rosei - Rose's Ticktrefoil

This species has the smallest flowers in the Desmodium genus in the Catalina mountains. It grows in the mid elevations and blooms in late Summer and early Fall. *Desmodium* comes from a Greek word meaning *chain*, referring to the way the fruits are connected together. They have burs which make them catch on to passing animals.

Lotus humistratus (Hosackia brachycarpus) - Foothill Deervetch
This is a low lying, low elevation plant that blooms in the Spring and
early Summer. The flowers are very small. This plant is easy to step on
without even noticing it.

Fabaceae - Bean Family

Macroptilium gibbosifolium - Variableleaf Bushbean, Wild Beanvine
This mid elevation plant tends to lie flat on the ground. It is a late Summer
to Fall bloomer. I first saw it in the Gordon Hirabayashi parking lot in the
Catalina Mountains.

Marina parryi - Parry's False Prairie-clover
This low elevation plant flowers in the late Spring and early Summer. Note how the tops of the flowers are blue and the bottoms white. The plants can be more than three feet tall.

Fabaceae - Bean Family

Rhynchosia senna - Texas Snoutbean
This mid elevation plant has a long blooming season from Spring into Fall. The plant is a climbing vine, with leaves in groups of three, and quite small flowers.

Trifolium pinetorum - Pine Clover
This high elevation plant is one that you are likely to walk on without even noticing the flowers. Plants are low growing and bloom most of the year.

Fabaceae - Bean Family

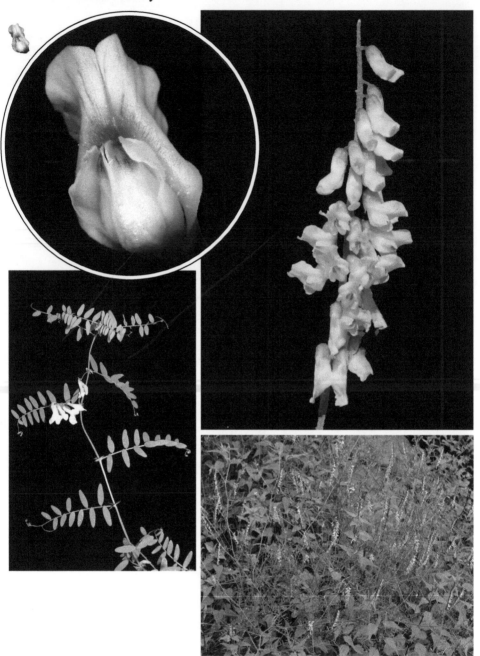

Vicia pulchella - Sweetclover Vetch, Showy Vetch
This high elevation plant blooms from Summer into Fall. The botanical name means "most beautiful", though I find it less attractive than the American Vetch (*Vicia americana*). A close examination reveals interesting blue markings on the flowers.

Quercus emoryi - Emory Oak
This mostly mid elevation tree blooms in the Spring. The arrows on the middle picture point out the male catkins in the upper right corner, and two female flowers in the lower left. This is an evergreen oak. Most of the local oaks have this combination of visible catkins of yellow flowers, and nearly invisible red female flowers.

Frasera speciosa (Swertia radiata) - Elkweed, Deers Ears, Green Gentian

This high elevation plant is in foliage with very large leaves year after year. Then one Spring it sends up an enormous stalk, sometimes eight feet tall, with many flower stems radiating out from its central stalk. In my experience plants that do not put up a flowering stalk in May will not be blooming that year. Since the flowers are mostly pale green, they are not very noticeable even though they are fairly large. This is one of those flowers that is worth a closer look.

Eucrypta micrantha - Dainty Desert Hideseed
This is a small, low elevation plant that blooms mostly in the Spring. It has a pleasant smell and is sticky. The botanical name means: "Well-hidden small flower" - making it a perfect candidate for this book.

Juglans major - Arizona Walnut
This is a mid elevation tree that grows near streams. It flowers mostly in
the Spring. The male flowers hang down in catkins. The female flowers are
much smaller, in the shape of two feathers. The right hand picture shows
them both on one branch, the female at the top.

Agastache breviflora - Trans-Pecos Giant Hyssop
This high elevation plant flowers in Summer and Fall. Plants are about a
foot or two tall. The individual flowers are worth a closer look.

113

Clinopodium vulgare - Wild Basil
This is a high elevation plant that lives in moist places. It flowers in Summer and Fall.

Hedeoma dentata - Toothleaf False Pennyroyal
This is mostly a mid elevation plant that blooms in late Summer and Fall.
It can grow to a foot tall. "Hedeoma" in Greek means "sweet smelling".
There are four other species in the Catalina mountains.

Hedeoma hyssopifolia - Mock Pennyroyal
This high elevation plant flowers in Summer and Fall. It is the most common Hedeoma in the Catalina mountains. It can often be seen on trails where few other wildflowers are blooming.

Hyptis emoryi - Desert Lavender
This is a low elevation shrub that grows near streams. It flowers almost
any time of the year. The flowers are difficult to spot since they are blue
and small compared to the size of the plant.

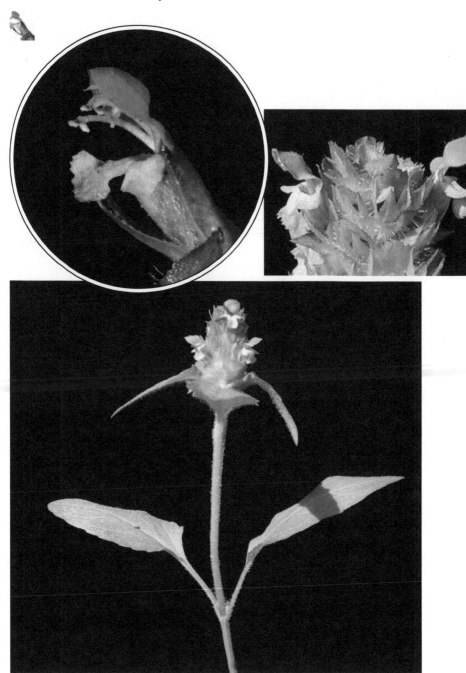

Prunella vulgaris - Self-heal
This high elevation plant flowers much of the year. It grows in moist
places. Plants are about a foot or two tall. It has been used as an herbal
medicine.

Salvia columbariae - Chia
This annual low elevation plant has clumps of flowers and leaves along
its one stalk. It blooms Spring into Summer. The blue flowers have yellow
pollen at their tips as can be seen in the picture above.

119

Lamiaceae - Mint Family

Trichostema arizonicum - Arizona Bluecurls
This mid elevation plant blooms in the Summer and Fall. Its flowers, while
not particularly small, are definitely worth looking at more closely.

Ayenia filiformis - Trans-Pecos Ayenia
This low elevation plant flowers much of the year. It is a medium sized
plant with tiny flowers at the base of the leaves, as can be seen in the left
middle picture. The fruits (middle left and right) are larger than the flowers.

Molluginaceae - Carpetweed Family

Mollugo verticillata - Green Carpetweed
This is a low to high elevation plant living on moist soils. It blooms in Summer and Fall. The small plants sometimes form a carpet of green. My hand in the middle picture gives an idea of the size of the plant and how small the flowers are.

Monotropa hypopitys - Pinesap
This high elevation parasitic plant blooms mostly in Summer. It does
not have chlorophyl, and so is not green. The red stalk comes out of the
ground and later its top droops.

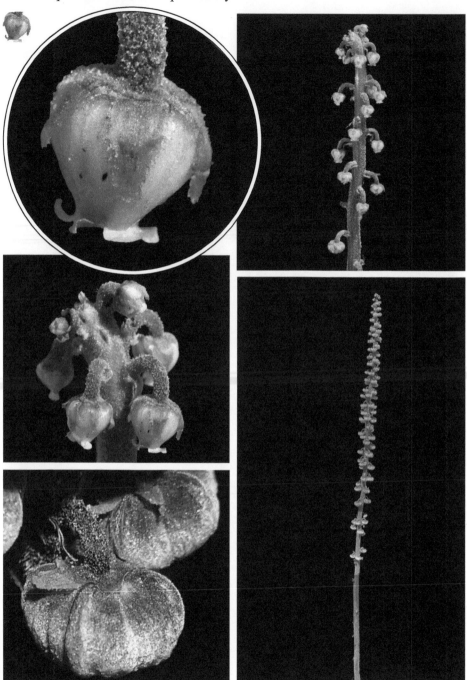

Pterospora andromedea - Woodland Pinedrops
This is a very rarely seen high elevation plant that blooms in Summer and early Fall. It grows in forest areas, living off other plants. It does not have leaves of its own. The one on the right was over three feet tall.

Cistanthe monandra - Common Pussy Paws
This is mostly a low elevation plant lying flat on the desert floor. It
blooms in Winter into Spring. It has fleshy leaves, and tiny flowers.

Claytonia perfoliata - Miner's Lettuce
This is a low to mid elevation plant that grows near streams. It blooms in Winter and Spring. The name *perfoliata (*which means *through the leaves)* refers to the way the flowers come out of the center of the leaf.

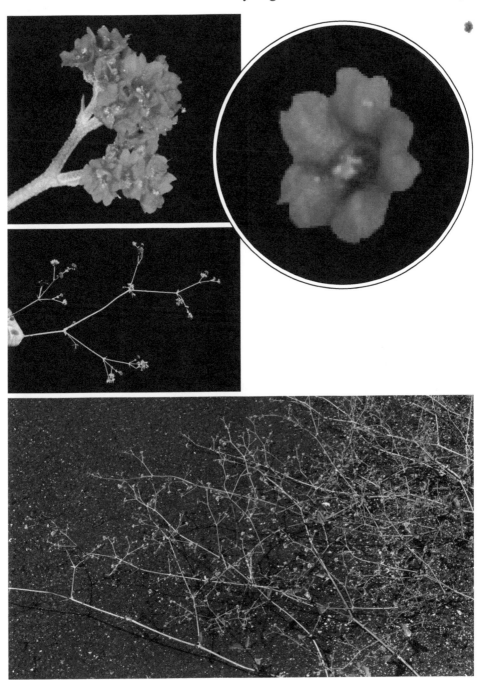

Boerhavia coccinea - Scarlet Spiderling
This low to mid elevation plant grows flat on the ground, spreading to
eight feet or more in diameter. It blooms Spring to Fall, but mostly in Fall.
The flower clusters are quite small, and each flower smaller still.

Boerhavia coulteri - Coulter's Spiderling
This is a low elevation plant that blooms in Summer. The plants are a foot or two high, and the flower clusters quite small.

Boerhavia erecta - Erect Spiderling
This mid elevation plant flowers in Summer and Fall. It is a medium sized plant with tiny flowers at the end of the stems, as can be seen in the right middle picture. The fruits are larger than the flowers.

129

Gaura hexandra ssp gracilis - Harlequinbush
This is a high elevation plant that blooms most of the year. It grows a foot or two tall, with relatively small flowers that are worth a closer look. The longest extension is the style with the stigma at the end, looking a little like a gold crown. The anthers are the brown tips at the end of the white filaments.

Orobanche cooperi - Desert Broomrape
This is a low elevation parasitic plant that blooms in Winter and Spring.
The leaves, shown in the middle picture, are more gray than green and
very hairy. The first time I saw one I thought it might be a pine cone rest-
ing on the ground.

Rivina humilis - Rougeplant, Pigeon Berry
This is a mid elevation plant that likes to be near water. It flowers in Summer and Fall. The plant is especially striking when it is in flower and has its beautiful red fruit at the same time.

Plantago ovata - Desert Indianwheat
This is a low elevation plant that blooms in Spring. The flower stalks are visible, but it takes a closer look to see the delicate, diaphanous flowers.

Plantaginaceae - Plantain Family

Plantago patagonica - Woolly Plantain
This low to mid elevation plant flowers in Spring and early Summer. The pale pink flowers are lined up along the flowering stalk as can be seen in the middle left picture.

Gilia flavocincta ssp australis - Lesser Yellowthroat Gilia
This is a small low to mid elevation plant that blooms in Spring. As can
be seen from the pictures, the color varies. This and the next Gilia have
cobwebby hairs as shown in the middle right picture. It has a yellow
throat,which is what *flavocincta* means.

135

Gilia mexicana - El Paso Gilia

This low to mid elevation plant is similar to *Gilia flavocincta* (p.135). It also blooms in Spring and has flowers that can be pale blue or white with a yellow throat.

Ipomopsis multiflora - Manyflowered Ipomopsis
This mostly mid elevation plant blooms from Summer into Fall. It is nota-
ble for its blue anthers. The flowers may be blue or purple (or even white).

Linanthus bigelovii - Bigelow's Linanthus

This is a low to mid elevation plant that blooms at night in Spring. The stems and leaves are thread-like, and so it is difficult to sort it out from the surrounding foliage. Since the flowers do not open until the evening, it is rarely seen in bloom.

Microsteris gracilis - Slender Phlox
This is an early Spring flower that grows mostly in mid elevations. The plant is quite small. The flowers may be pink or white or a combination of the two.The middle left picture shows a portion of a penny to get an idea of the size. The right middle shows one in my hand with both pink and white flowers on the same plant.

139

Monnina wrightii - Blue Pygmyflower
This is a mid to high elevation plant that blooms in Summer and Fall. It can get lost in other foliage, as seen in the bottom left picture. Individual flowers have a curious shape, like a blue and yellow boat.

Polygala obscura - Velvetseed Milkwort
This curious small plant grows mostly in mid elevations in Summer and
Fall. It ranges in color from blue to purple. I nearly stepped on one once
since it was in the middle of the Arizona Trail, somewhat protected by a
rock.

141

Eriogonum deflexum - Flatcrown Buckwheat, Skeleton Weed
This low elevation plant is medium size - a foot or so tall, but has quite
small flower clusters. It blooms most of the year. From a distance it has an
airy look to it.

Eriogonum fasciculatum - Eastern Mojave Buckwheat, Flattop Buckwheat
This is a mid elevation plant that is abundant along the Mt. Lemmon highway. It blooms in Spring into Summer. The fruit is a beautiful rust color
which persists into Fall. The plants in the bottom picture have flowers
(pale pink) and fruit (rust) at the same time.

143

Polygonaceae - Buckwheat Family

Eriogonum polycladon - Sorrel Buckwheat
This is a low to mid elevation plant that blooms in late Summer and Fall.
The bottom picture shows how abundant it can be, casting a pink haze
over the landscape. The pink comes from the flower buds (top right picture) or the fruit. In the middle right picture the plant is in bloom, so you
can see how unspectacular it is until you take a closer look.

Fallopia (Polygonum) convolvulus - Black Bindweed, Cornbind
This is a mid to high elevation, non-native vine. It blooms Spring and
Summer, with tiny white flowers.

Polygonum aviculare - Prostrate Knotweed
This is a high elevation plant that blooms with tiny flowers more or less all year and gets walked on a lot. It is non-native, and forms large mats on dirt roads and trails.

Polygonum douglasii ssp. johnstonii – Johnston's Knotweed
This is a high elevation plant that blooms in Summer and Fall. It is very difficult to see since it is thin and has tiny flowers.

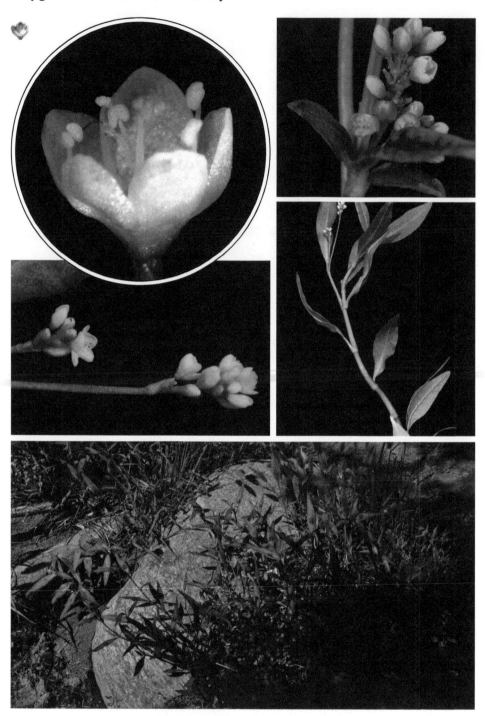

Polygonum (Persicaria) lapathifolia - Curlytop Knotweed
This is a water-loving, low elevation plant that blooms most of the year.

Rumex altissimus - Pale Dock

This is a mid to high elevation plant that blooms most of the year. Its flowers are hard to see. The plant is very colorful with red fruits (inset lower left). It has separate male and female flowers on the same plant. The female is in the right top picture.

149

Polygonaceae - Buckwheat Family

Rumex obtusifolius - Bitter Dock
This tall, non-native, mostly high elevation plant grows best in moist places, and can bloom almost any time from Spring to Fall. The flowers are very small, with yellow stamens (male) and white stigmas (female) in the same flower head. The golden fruits are interesting.

Androsace septentrionalis - Pygmyflower Rockjasmine
This tiny high elevation plant blooms most of the year. It has basal leaves, and small white flowers on long stalks. There is a very similar plant, Western Rockjasmine (*Androsace occidentalis*) that grows in mid elevations, blooming only in Spring.

Ranunculaceae - Buttercup Family

Myosurus cupulatus - Arizona Mousetail
This very curious plant grows in damp places in mid elevations. It is a
Spring bloomer. The flowers begin small, but as they turn to fruit the "tail"
gets longer and longer. The picture with the penny gives an idea of size.
The middle right picture shows the flower from two different angles.

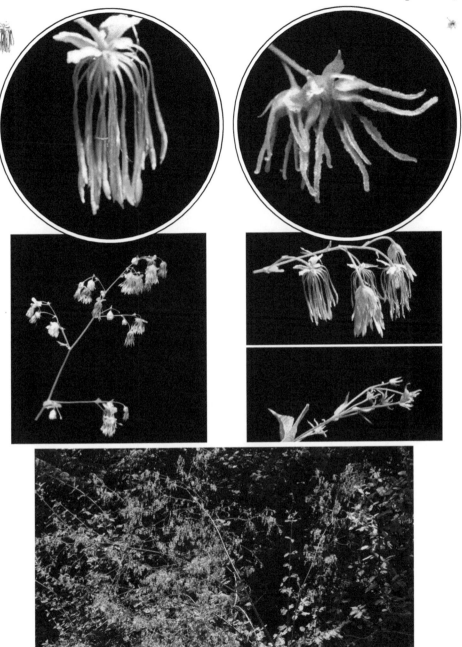

Thalictrum fendleri - Fendler's Meadow-Rue

This high elevation plant is dioecious, meaning it has separate male and female plants. The top pictures show a male flower on the left and a female on the right. The right middle picture shows both at the same scale, male above the line and female below. Male tassels are fairly easy to see. The female flowers are harder to spot. Meadow Rue is related to Columbines and has similar leaves.

153

Rhamnaceae - Buckthorn Family

Ceanothus fendleri - Fendler's Ceanothus, Fendler Deerbrush
This mid to high elevation plant blooms most of the year. It is a favorite of
many butterflies. The top left picture shows an individual flower. The red
fruits are often on the plant at the same time as flower clusters. There is
another Deerbrush on the mountain (*Ceanothus integerrimus*) that is more
spectacular but not nearly as abundant.

154

Condalia warnockii - Kearney Snakewood
This is a large, low elevation shrub that blooms in Summer and Fall. Its fruits start out yellow and turn red then almost black. It has very dense foliage.

Rhamnus ilicifolia - Hollyleaf Redberry, Hollyleaf Buckthorn
This evergreen shrub grows mostly in the mid elevations blooming from
Spring into Summer. The berries turn yellow then bright red as in the
middle right picture. The bottom picture shows the plant in full fruit.

Holodiscus dumosus - Rockspirea, Mountain Spray
This high elevation shrub blooms in Summer and Fall. It looks very pink
when it is in bud and when it is in fruit, but the flowers are white. They
come in long clusters so it is not easy to see what an individual flower
looks like.

Sanguisorba minor - Small Burnet

This mid and high elevation plant is not native. It blooms in late Spring and Summer. From a distance it looks uninteresting. On closer look one can see that the flower heads are topped with red feathery female flowers. Below them are pods containing the male flowers which burst out on long stalks.

Diodia teres - Poorjoe, Buttonweed

This mid elevation plant blooms in Summer and early Fall. It is a small plant, as can be seen from the upper left hand picture, with white to pink flowers. The flowers are tucked into the junction of stem and leaf and are easy to miss.

159

Galium fendleri - Fendler's Bedstraw

"*Arizona Flora*", by Kearney and Peebles, lists 17 Galiums. There are five included in this book. Fendler's is a high elevation plant that blooms in Summer and early Fall. It is interesting because it is dioecious, and has pale yellow flowers. The split photograph shows male flowers above, and female flowers and fruit below. The plants are soft to the touch.

Galium mexicanum ssp. asperrimum - Mexican Bedstraw
This mid and high elevation plant blooms in Summer and early Fall. It is
a fairly large plant that often supports itself on other plants. Its leaves are
very sticky. The anthers change from yellow to brown or black after they
have lost their pollen.

Galium microphyllum - Bracted Bedstraw
This is a mid to high elevation plant that can bloom from Spring to Fall.
"Microphyllum" means "very small leaves" and the flowers are even
smaller, as in the photograph with its shadow on a penny. The plants may
be a foot and a half tall. The tiny flowers start off pale pink and turn deep
red. The bottom right picture shows a plant against the base of a Ponderosa Pine. The fruits are much larger than the flowers.

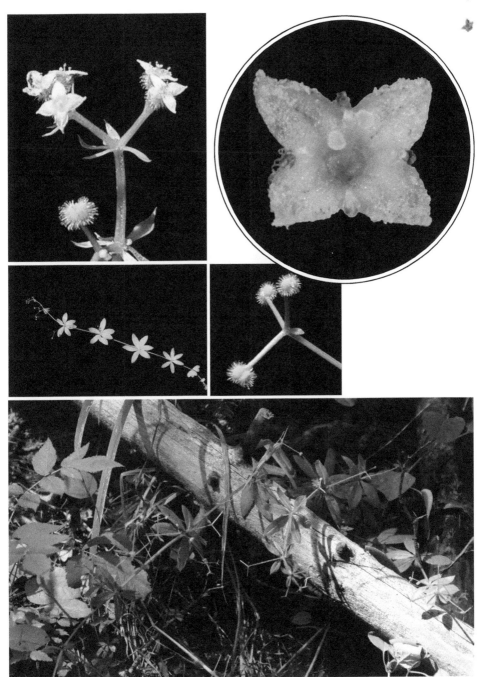

Galium triflorum - Fragrant Bedstraw
This high elevation plant blooms in Summer and early Fall. It is a small plant, with larger leaves than many of the other bedstraws. The flowers come in groups of three as the botanical name suggests. It tends to lie on the ground, unable to support its own weight.

Galium wrightii - Wright's Bedstraw
This is a mid to high elevation plant that blooms in Summer and Fall.
The plants have very tiny red flowers which are difficult to see. When it's
in fruit it is more noticeable. The middle left picture shows the plant in
bloom. The middle right picture shows it in fruit. The plant in the bottom
picture has flowers and fruit.

Hedyotis greenei - Greene's Starviolet
This mid to high elevation plant blooms in late Summer and Fall. It is a small plant, with flowers at the tops of the branches. The bottom right picture shows a group of plants on a hillside. Note the beautiful markings on the bracts in the top left picture.

Houstonia wrightii - Pygmy Bluet
This is a high elevation plant which forms mats that may bloom almost
any of the flowering months of the year. Its flowers may be white, pink or
blue. There are many trails where it is hard to walk without stepping on
one of these charming plants.

Thamnosma texana - Rue of the Mountains, Dutchman's Breeches
This is a low to mid elevation plant which has red flowers that bloom
in Spring and Summer. Their yellow stamens are sometimes concealed,
sometimes protruding. I photographed this in a wash in Saguaro National
Park East. The edge of my thumb in the middle picture gives an idea of
the size of the flowers. One common name, 'Dutchman's Breeches', refers
to the shape of the fruit, shown on the lower right hand picture.

167

Santalaceae [Viscaceae] - Sandalwood Family

Phoradendron californicum - Mesquite Mistletoe, Desert Mistletoe
This is a mostly low elevation plant that blooms in Winter and Spring. It attaches itself to trees in the desert, such as Acacia, Mesquite, Palo Verde and others. The flowers have a pleasant frangrance. Individual flowers are very tiny. Note the top left is the male and has anthers. Top right is female. The fruits are edible.

Phoradendron juniperinum - Juniper Mistletoe
This is a mid elevation plant that grows on the Alligator Juniper *(Juniperus deppeanna* p.197). It blooms in Spring and Summer. Plants are either male or female. The flowers have a pleasant fragrance. Top left shows a male flower and below it a male plant. Top right shows a female flower and below it a female plant with a fruit below that. The center picture shows a female branch. The fruits are edible.

169

Sapindaceae - Soapberry Family

Dodonaea viscosa - Hopbush
This is a low to mid elevation shrub. It is one of those plants that may be
dioecious, or rarely polygamodioecious. Flowers may appear in almost
any month of the year. The top right picture is of a male flower, and on the
left the female. The fruits are attractive and easy to see.

170

Saxifraga eriophora - Redfuzz Saxifrage
This high elevation plant has leaves all year long. It blooms in early
Spring. I have seen it blooming amid patches of snow. The stems and buds
are red.

171

Castilleja exserta - Exserted Indian Paintbrush, Owl's Clover
This is a low elevation plant that blooms in Spring, sometimes in great
quantities as part of the desert in bloom. The close-up shows that the
flower is something like an owl's face.

*Penstemon discolo*r - Catalina Beardtongue
This mid elevation plant is fairly small and through much of the year looks like a few dried up sticks. It blooms in May and June and is well worth a closer look. The color of the flower varies from white to pale blue with red markings and a beautiful yellow beard.

Scrophulariaceae - Figwort Family

Scrophularia parviflora - Pineland Figwort
This is a fairly large high elevation plant that blooms Summer and Fall. It usually has rust-red flowers. Occasionally the flowers are pure white, as in the smaller picture. The stems are square and the leaves opposite so it looks like it might be in the mint family, but it is not.

Veronica peregrina - Neckweed
This is a low to mid elevation plant that blooms much of the year but
depends on moisture. It thrives along stream beds. The fruits are like
beautiful little hearts.

Simmondsiaceae - Jojoba Family

Simmondsia chinensis - Jojoba
This is an evergreen, low elevation shrub. It blooms mostly in February,
on separate male and female plants. The left middle picture has the female
and male flowers side by side at the same scale. The fruit is very useful as
a source of oil (middle right picture).

Lycium exsertum - Arizona Desert-thorn, Wolfberry
This is a mostly low elevation shrub that blooms in Winter and Spring.
The upper left picture is taken looking down at the face of the flower.

Aloysia wrightii - Wright's Beebrush, Oreganillo
This is a low to mid elevation shrub that blooms in Summer and Fall. Its leaves have a very pleasant odor, even when they are all dried up in winter. The tiny flowers form a row at the tips of the branches.

Plectritis ciliosa - Longspur Seablush

This is a small, mid elevation flower that grows in damp places. Plectritis means plaited and ciliosa means fringed. It flowers in late Winter into Spring. It usually has one flower stalk, and paired leaves that hug the stem. In a wet season it can carpet the ground.

Verbena bracteata - Bigbract Verbena
This mid to high elevation plant blooms much of the year. It is a low-growing plant, with rather small flowers.

Viola umbraticola - Ponderosa Violet, Blue Violet
There are two Violet species in the Catalina Mountains, both at high
elevations. The Canadian Violet (*Viola canadensis*) blooms most of the
year from Spring to Fall. The Blue Violet blooms with regular flowers
in Spring, and has another set of totally enclosed flowers (cleistogamic)
in Summer. The red circles in the bottom picture surround these hiddden
flowers. The top left picture shows that this enclosed flower did get fertil-
ized and developed fruit. (See page 70 for another example.)

181

Vitaceae - Grape Family

Parthenocissus vitacea - Woodbine,Virginia Creeper

This mid elevation vine grows to enormous size, climbing trees or spreading out on the canyon floor. It blooms mostly in the Spring. The flowers are quite small. The upper right picture shows many buds, and a few flowers that have lost their anthers and petals. It has deep blue fruit and its leaves turn a beautiful red in the Fall.

Monocots or Monocotyldeons

Angiosperms (plants that produce flowers and seeds) are divided into eudicots (or dicots) and monocots. Monocots have a single seed leaf (cotyledon). Grasses and grasslike plants are monocots. Their flowers are rarely seen. They are the most abundant of the monocots, forming one of the largest of all plant families. When we study them we find that their various parts have an entirely new set of names, but the fundamental quality of having a part that produces pollen (the anthers), and parts that receive pollen (the stigmas), is the same as other more obvious flowering plants. Orchids, agaves, lilies and some other flowers are also monocots.

Cyperaceae - Sedge Family

Carex senta - Swamp Carex

This mid elevation perennial plant grows in stream beds. It blooms Spring and Summer and is one of the grass-like plants on the mountain. The tops of the spikes have the male flowers (left top), and beneath them the female (right top). The middle right picture shows the male flowers and female flowers together, the male at the top and female at the bottom left.

Cyperus fendlerianus - Fendler's Flat Sedge
This mid to high elevation perennial plant is fairly common in the mountains. It blooms in Summer and into Fall. The stems have edges (Sedges have edges). The lower right picture is the view looking straight down at the plant. The flowers are very tiny and are the small parts of the picture in the circle.

185

Juncaceae - Rush Family

Juncus marginatus - Grassleaf Rush

This mid to high elevation plant blooms in Summer and Fall. As the name
suggests, it looks very much like a grass except for the deep brown clusters on the tops of the stems. The stems are round and solid with the flowers tucked into the top. This plant needs to be near water.

186

Dasylirion wheeleri - Common Sotol, Desert Spoon
This is a large, mostly mid elevation, species that has separate male and female plants. The flower stalks usually appear in Sumnmer and early Fall, and can be up to twelve feet tall. They sometimes remain on the plant more than a year after blooming. Each flower stalk has thousands of individual flowers. Though the stalks are highly visible, the individual flowers are not. The plants on the left are male, and those on the right female.

187

Nolina microcarpa - Sacahuista, Beargrass

This is a mostly mid elevation evergreen shrub with separate male and female plants. The flower stalks usually appear in Summer and early Fall, Each flower stalk has thousands of individual flowers. Though the stalks are highly visible, the individual flowers are not. The plants on the left are male, and those on the right female.

Corallorhiza wisteriana
Spring Coralroot

Corallorhiza maculata
Spotted Coralroot

Corallorhiza striata
Striped Coralroot

These three high elevation orchids grow in the woods. The first is mostly a Spring bloomer. The other two bloom more in the Summer. They have no chlorophyl and so depend on fungus and roots of trees for their life.

Malaxis abieticola,
M.tenuis
Slender-flowered
Malaxis

Malaxis corymbosa
Huachuca
Adder's Mouth

Malaxis soulei
Chiricahua
Adder's Mouth

These three orchids all bloom at high elevations in summer, a few weeks after the onset of summer rains, and possibly into Fall. These usually have just one leaf. They are mostly a Mexican species, reaching their northern-most limits in Arizona and New Mexico.

Platanthera limosa - Thurber's Bog Orchid
This high elevation plant loves wet places. It blooms in Summer and Fall.
It is the largest orchid in the Santa Catalina mountains. In some places, as
in the lowest picture, it forms a large colony.

Schiedeella arizonica - Parasitic Lady's Tresses, Fallen Lady's Tresses
This high elevation plant blooms in late May in deep woods. It is very
small. The leaves appear after the plant has finished blooming. Note the
touch of orange in the flower.

Muhlenbergia rigens - Deergrass

Grasses are among the most abundant of the "invisible" flowers. We show just one to give an idea of what grass flowers look like. This low and mid elevation perennial grass blooms after Summer rains. The flower stalks are loaded with small flowers. The portion of a penny gives an idea of how tiny and abundant they are. Male flowers carry the pollen, and come in a variety of colors, often pale yellow as in this one. Female flowers are often like little feathers. They also come in a variety of colors, in this case white, turning black after pollination. It lives in stream beds.

Gymnosperms

Gymnosperm is a word from the Greek gymnospermatos, which in turn is a combination of gymnos meaning naked and sperma meaning seed. This category of plants has seeds that are not surrounded by a fruit or ovary. Most of the plants are evergreen, including pines, firs, yews, and so on. The fruit is usually a woody structure. Pine cones are an example. Gymnosperms do not have true flowers. Instead they have pollen-bearing cones, and seed cones that receive the pollen. After they receive the pollen they develop into actual cones with naked seeds in them. Many of these seeds have wings so that they spin as they fall down from the tree.

Hesperocyparis arizonica - Arizona Cypress
This mid elevation tree has a great many pollen cones in Spring, as seen in the lower left picture. Each pollen cone is very small, and expands to release the pollen grains. The middle left picture shows that the fruit does the same thing. The seed cone begins very small. After being pollinated it grows into a round fruit. When ripe this fruit expands to realease the seeds. The process takes two years.

Juniperus deppeana - Alligator Juniper
This mid to high elevation tree blooms in Winter and Spring. The pollen
cones are abundant and give the tree a look of being covered with tiny
brown spots. The upper right picture shows one of those cones with the
pollen just starting to emerge. The seed cones (not shown) receive the
pollen. The middle right picture shows the fruit. See page p.169 for the
mistletoe that grows on this species of tree.

197

Abies concolor - White Fir

This high elevation evergreen tree blooms in late Spring and early Summer. The top left picture shows the pollen cone with its grains. The right top picture shows two male pollen cones with a red seed cone (female) between them. The fruits stand upright and grow at the top of the tree. The middle left picture shows how they consist of layers, each one of which has seeds at the center. The fruits disintegrate on the tree and release winged seeds to helicopter down.

198

Pinus ponderosa - Ponderosa Pine
This mid to high elevation evergreen tree blooms in Spring. The pollen cones are
abundant. At first they are shaped something like a football covered with scales
which are tightly closed. When they mature the scales open, releasing their pollen
(picture middle left). Then they fall from the tree forming a carpet of what look
like tiny dried up brown worms.The seed cones start out a beautiful red, and turn
purple or lilac as they mature.

Pinus strobiformis - Southwestern White Pine
This high elevation evergreen tree blooms in June. The pollen cones start out pale yellow and turn brown with age. They can be abundant, as in the middle left picture. The seed cones start out purple and turn red as they grow. This Pine has the largest cones of all pine species in Southern Arizona.

Pseudotsuga menziesii - Rocky Mountain Douglas-fir.
This mid to high elevation evergreen tree blooms in Spring and Summer.
The middle right picture shows the seed cone at the tip of the branch, with a cluster of pollen cones beneath it. The lower right picture shows that maturing fruit, which eventually turns brown. The pollen cones start out yellow and also turn brown.

201

Index

202

P

Q

R

S

Photo by Owen Rose

About the Author

After a career in pastoral work and teaching in England, Canada and Pennsylvania, Frank moved to Tucson with his wife, Louise, in 1982. He served for 21 years as Pastor of Sunrise Chapel. He is a past President of the Southern Arizona Watercolor Guild and of the Tucson Ministerial Association. In July, 2003, Frank retired from pastoral work. He now devotes his time to writing, hiking, searching out Wildflowers, and painting.

Additional resources for plant identification:
bonap.org
swbiodiversity.org/seinet
plants.sc.egov.usda.gov
plantID.net
fireflyforest.com/flowers
Visit Frank's blog at franksrose.com

CPSIA information can be obtained
at www.ICGtesting.com
Printed in the USA
BVHW09s1232260818
525262BV00004B/9/P

9 781732 540200